COGNITIVE BEHAVIORAL THERAPY

WORKBOOK FOR

SEX & PORNOGRAPHY ADDICTION

CBT Worksheet with Tools to Deal with Stress, Anxiety, Anger, Control Mood, Learn New Behaviors & Regulate Emotions

DR PHIL MICHIGAN

© 2020 Dr Phil Michigan

All rights reserved.

You are welcome to join the Fan's Corner, here

Disclaimer
The advice and strategies found within may not be suitable for every situation. This work is sold with the understanding that neither the author nor the publisher is held responsible for the results accrued from the advice in this book.

D1511789

Cognitive Behavioral Therapy Workbook

Cognitive-behavioral therapy is a type of therapy that tends to focus on the belief and thoughts of an individual, which is what helps to make it a very popular and effective technique in the treatment of problems relating to various ailments including this one. Although treatment of various ailments including this one is possible with many other methods, many experts find that CBT therapy is probably a more effective option for treating various ailments including this one. When CBT therapy is used in the management of problems, it tends to treat more than just the symptoms associated with the problem by focusing on how to uncover the underlying issues that are causing your worries and fears. CBT helps you learn ways of relaxing and looking at situations in a different way that is not as frightening as the way you have grown accustomed to and instead help you to develop better coping and problem-solving skills. With CBT, you become equipped with the tools you need to overcome problems and cope with them.

This workbook will help you deal with your challenges and problem by giving you a template that is structured to make handling it easy. It uses different steps that get you to focus on your self-beliefs and how to devise ways to challenge some of these unhelpful self-beliefs blocking your objective view of situations. By following through with this, you will be able to identify situations that usually serve as triggers for your actions and the kinds of thought they elicit in you. It is structured in such a way to make the different sessions with your therapist worthwhile and help you develop effective self-control and coping techniques.

Using this workbook, you will be able to recognize the consequences of your condition and come up with alternative thinking to overcome the automatic negative thoughts associated with your condition.

It doesn't stop there, the skills developed here can easily be applied to other aspects of life. Cognitive-behavioral therapy is a type of therapy that involves a great deal of interaction to properly identify unhelpful thoughts and beliefs that contribute towards your abuse of drugs and alcohol so as to come up with solutions to your dependency. Such common unhelpful thoughts related to dependency can include, but not limited to:

- Things always get screwed up with me, I'm such a loser.
- Something is wrong with me
- I can't do it. I feel too anxious to make an attempt.

- I don't know Why I am not able to control my situation

As soon as you are able to identify such thoughts and beliefs, you will then proceed to challenge such thoughts using the tools you will find in this book so that you can come up with more objective and realistic thoughts that you will find more helpful. Some of that helpful fact-based evidence you can use to challenge your unhelpful negative thoughts can include:

- Everyone makes mistakes and that includes me, I'm only human.
- I can try to fix the situation and learn from this experience.
- Other people feel anxious too.
- It's not life threatening and doesn't mean I have to stop.
- Being anxious is part of life, doesn't stop me from still going to the party.

With CBT you will become better equipped to identify and deal with triggers that usually make you indulge, such as:

- When Stressed
- Faced with situation
- When you find yourself in new environments

At the end of your CBT therapy and with the help of this workbook, you will now be better equipped to avoid certain triggers and learn how to effectively cope with unavoidable situations and emotions.

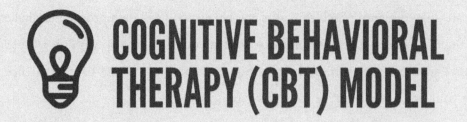

COGNITIVE BEHAVIORAL THERAPY (CBT) MODEL

1 SITUATION
Identify situations that trigger you. Seek to know why they are able to trigger you

2 THOUGHTS
What was the first thought that entered your mind? This can also be referred to as your initial thoughts.

3 EMOTIONS (FEELINGS)
How did the thought make you feel? How intense was this feeling?

4 BEHAVIOR (REACTION)
The action that is taken as a result of your emotions or how felt.

YOUR CBT FIRST AID

SIMPLE CBT MODEL

Relevant Life History

Write out details of aspects of your life that you feel has affected you the most. Write it out with as much as possible.

Include even those aspects that you are not sure are relevant to what you are talking about. If you are unable to keep the record organized, do not worry, just write it the best way that seems to work for you as if you were telling someone the history of your life.

What Are Core Beliefs?

Core beliefs are assumptions and thoughts we have about ourselves, the people around us, and the world. These beliefs are usually deep-seated and often go unnoticed even though they tend to affect our lives constantly. It is mostly as a result of the belief that our thoughts and feelings affect us to such an extent that threatens to derail our success and happiness.

Common Core Beliefs That Can Hinder You

The belief that something is wrong with You

Core beliefs like this make you suffer from low self-esteem. It often prevents you from wanting to have any sort of friendship with people preferring instead to stay on your own, so that others do not notice what you perceive to be the things wrong with you.

Beliefs like:

"I'm broken"

"Nothing about me is good, everything is wrong with me"

"I think I am no good"

"I think I am stupid and cannot make any right decision"

"I think I am worthless"

"Everyone around me has a better life than me"

"No one really knows I exist"

"I am such a bad person beyond redemption"

"I am a complete"

"Nothing I do ever goes right or works"

No One Can Love Me

Similar to the first one is the feeling of being unloved or unlovable. This can sometimes force you to avoid being in relationships so as to avoid experiencing your belief that you are not lovable or in some cases can make you try to force yourself on others even when they treat you badly or abuse you emotionally.

Thoughts associated with this belief include:

"I'm better off being on my own"

"I think I am boring"

"Everyone hates me"

"I can do things on my own"

"No one wants to understand me"

"Nobody wants me around them"

My Display of Love Seems Drive People Away from Me

Those with this kind of core belief often find themselves being scared of being rejected, prompting them to end relationships very early even when there is no need to do so.

This core belief is commonly associated with thoughts like:

"People end up abandoning me anyway"

"Loving someone is dangerous"

"When you love someone, you will get hurt"

"I have to be worthy to be loved"

"I can't find happiness if I am not with someone"

"People reject me"

We Live in a Dangerous World

This core belief is often associated with anxiety and fear so that your thoughts are only seen from a position of how to play safe based on your overexaggerated perception of danger. This will often prevent you from living up to your potential in life. Sometimes, it can lead you to be a control freak who wants to always be in control of everything without letting things go.

This belief will often result in thoughts like:

"No one is worthy of trust"

"Everyone is out to get me"

"I am not as powerful as others"

"I am helpless in most situations"

"I do not have the strength for anything"

"Being in control is the only way to survive"

"I have to always be on my guard"

"I should never leave myself vulnerable"

"I don't ever want to reveal who I really am"

I do not Consider Myself Good Enough

This type of core belief will usually make you either have low self-esteem which can lead to depression or make you feign perfectionist in an attempt to try to hide your low self-esteem and fears. In some other cases, you may have even given up trying to make yourself feel worthy and instead allow other people to manipulate and abuse you.

Core beliefs like this will manifest in situations like:

"I am incapable of changing"

"I am unskilled"

"I am a loser"

"I can never win no matter what I do"

"I am a born failure"

"There is really no need to make further efforts"

I'm Weird

This core belief tends to make you suffer from an extreme form of loneliness even when living in the midst of people. It will feel as if you do not even understand yourself. The manifestations of these core beliefs are noticeable in statements like:

"I do not know where I am from"

"I do not belong here"

"I feel like I come from a different planet"

"No one understands me"

"Something is not right with"

I Will Do Anything to Be Liked

This often stems from a core belief associated with childhood that only made a child feel loved only when they were good or acted in good behavior. This will make you not to be able to have steady relationships and identity issues. Some of these core beliefs associated with this core belief include:

"No one likes sad people"

"I cannot have bad thoughts"

"I am not loved when I am angry"

"When I do bad things, means I am a bad person"

I am Always at Fault

This core belief makes you not to have personal boundaries and an inability to say no to others. You will probably have relationships that are codependent. Common thoughts associated with this include:

"I do not want to hurt others"

"I am always wrong"

"I need to try harder"

"When I love people well enough, I will be able to fix them"

"I have to help everyone who comes my way"

"I have to be perfect"

I am a very Special Person

This type of core belief often results in great narcissism and grandiosity. This can result in you manipulating others and making others around you feel inferior and uneasy to be in your presence. It will often result in your not ever experiencing any form of true love and intimacy. Thoughts associated with this core belief include:

"I should be entitled to more"

"I deserve to have more attention"

"I shouldn't be criticized"

"I am superior to others"

"I am more intelligent than others"

Why Core Beliefs are Important

If sufficient time is not taken to try to dig out and have our negative core beliefs questioned, they will be capable of affecting the different decisions we make.

Analyzing Core Beliefs

Analyzing core beliefs will help us understand how they impact on our self-esteem, image, and future expectations. Negative core beliefs will distort our perception of the world and the way we see others around us. By taking this step, it now becomes possible to identify the core beliefs that have found a way to affect our thoughts, emotions, and behaviors.

How to Identify your Personal Core Beliefs?

In order to make the process easier for you, there are a few examples of questions you can ask to help you identify your views about yourself, others and the world around you.

Questions to Ask Yourself

Am I clever, confident, attractive, ugly?

Am I good at what I do?

Am I a good and loving partner?

Am I a responsible parent?

Do I overly criticize and judge myself?

Do I consider myself better than everyone else?

Do I feel I do not deserve to be loved and be happy?

Do I feel unworthy of being wealthy?

Questions that Relate to Others

Do I consider others to be luckier than I am?

Do I always get the short end of the stick whereas others get the long end?

Do I consider others to be smarter than I am?

Do I consider life to be easier for others than it is for me?

Do I feel others are more favored than I am?

Do I feel others less attractive than I am?

Do I consider others to be inferior to me?

Is my view of others as though they are all irredeemably bad?

Or, do I view the world as if people are incapable of doing bad?

Questions on How You View the World

Do I use phrases like 'everyone' and 'no-one?'

Is my view of the world that of one homogenous entity of people?

Do I recognize the presence of a variety of people?

Is my view of the world as though only evil happening in the world?

Or do I see the world only from the perspective that only good things happen?

Do I have a very pessimistic perception of society?

Challenging your Core Beliefs

Many of the core beliefs we have, are neither true nor helpful, which is why a conscious effort has to be made to ensure that we challenge such beliefs and come up with ways to overcome them so that they do not overwhelm you. To evaluate and have your core belief challenged, you have to ask yourself a couple of questions. The essence of this exercise is to show that many of your unhelpful core beliefs are not only unhelpful but also not entirely true.

Questions to Challenge your Core Beliefs

What are my experiences that show that this belief isn't entirely true all the time?"

You use this exercise to list out as many of these experiences that you have. Make them as specific as possible in a factual way as if you were presenting it to a judge.

Do not forget to include even those experiences you are not sure are relevant to that scenario. When all the experiences have been listed, you can then proceed to develop an alternative and balanced core belief.

Next, you try and come up with what you consider to be more helpful and balanced core beliefs.

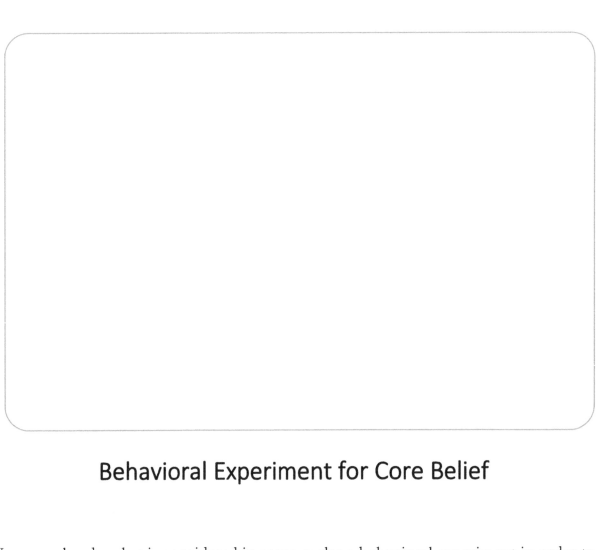

Behavioral Experiment for Core Belief

You can also do what is considered in some cycles a behavioral experiment in order to challenge the unhelpful core beliefs that are difficult to budge.

Aim of the Behavioral Experiment

The aim of this experiment is to help you determine how true your core beliefs are.

Methodology

The approach, in this case, will be to systematically and deliberately challenge your unhelpful core beliefs using a more scientific method and tools. In this approach, you will note down a specific unhelpful core belief you plan to test, then you identify the tasks that you feel will help you test those core beliefs better.

After that, you come up with a hypothesis or theory of what you expect the result to be at the end of the experiment. As you begin to undertake the earlier task you had planned, note down the actual result.

Next, you compare your actual result with the anticipated result, you documented in your hypothesis. Are there any deviations? Was the result as drastic and dramatic as you had anticipated it to be? Note down these observations.

Based on your experiment, come up with a more balanced belief that will be more helpful to you in such similar situations.

Write Down the Core Belief You Intend to Test

Note Down Tasks You Feel are Able to Help You Test Those Core Beliefs

Put Down the Kind of Results You Expect if The Core Beliefs are Really True

Carry Out the Tasks

Write Out What Really Happened as a Result of the Task

Compare the Actual Result with your Prediction

Note Down your Learning Point from the Experiment

Write Down What You Now Consider to be a New Helpful and More Balanced Belief That your Conclusion has Now Led You to Believe

ASSESSMENT OF PATIENT

Name of Professional

Session

Name of Patient

Date of Appointment

INTERACTION WITH PATIENT

VERDICT/ OBSERVATIONS

Cognitive Model

Situation

Events that serves
as a trigger

Thoughts

The way the situation
is interpreted

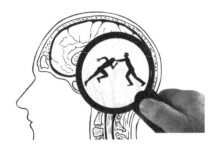

Emotions

The resultant feeling or
from the thoughts

Behavior

The action that results
from emotion

Thought Challenge

You can use this simple and effective approach to challenge your unhelpful thoughts. With this technique, you are able to view things from different perspectives using an evidence-based technique in the consideration of your various alternatives.

Rather than see this technique as just a form of positive affirmation, it is instead better considered as analyzing a thought objectively instead of accepting your thoughts to be pure facts or taking such facts to be true. Some of these thoughts tend to appear as facts which is why the act of challenging these thoughts is very important in trying to separate facts from friction.

Try and spend a lot of time on evidences that contradicts this kind of thoughts when using this worksheet.

What is the most intense and hot thought from the previous section you want to address?	
State the evidences you think supports this kind of thought?	

Do you have any evidence to contradict this thought?

How do you think you will feel, 6 months from now about this issue?

What alternative way of analyzing this situation can you think of?

What are the more objective, balanced and realistic way of viewing the situation?

Which of these do you consider more relevant?

How do you rate this new objective, balanced and realistic thought?

How does it make you now feel?

Is this an exercise you would want to try again? State your reason.

CBT General Worksheet

Describe the Situation	Note your Feelings and its Rating	Write your Automatic Negative Thoughts	Note Evidences Supporting your Thoughts	Evidences that do not Support your Thoughts	Resultant Balanced, Realistic or Objective Thought	How do you feel now?

Describe the Situation	Note your Feelings and its Rating	Write your Automatic Negative Thoughts	Note Evidences Supporting your Thoughts	Evidences that do not Support your Thoughts	Resultant Balanced, Realistic or Objective Thought	How do you feel now?

Describe the Situation	Note your Feelings and its Rating	Write your Automatic Negative Thoughts	Note Evidences Supporting your Thoughts	Evidences that do not Support your Thoughts	Resultant Balanced, Realistic or Objective Thought	How do you feel now?

Describe the Situation	Note your Feelings and its Rating	Write your Automatic Negative Thoughts	Note Evidences Supporting your Thoughts	Evidences that do not Support your Thoughts	Resultant Balanced, Realistic or Objective Thought	How do you feel now?

Describe the Situation	Note your Feelings and its Rating	Write your Automatic Negative Thoughts	Note Evidences Supporting your Thoughts	Evidences that do not Support your Thoughts	Resultant Balanced, Realistic or Objective Thought	How do you feel now?

Describe the Situation	Note your Feelings and its Rating	Write your Automatic Negative Thoughts	Note Evidences Supporting your Thoughts	Evidences that do not Support your Thoughts	Resultant Balanced, Realistic or Objective Thought	How do you feel now?

Describe the Situation	Note your Feelings and its Rating	Write your Automatic Negative Thoughts	Note Evidences Supporting your Thoughts	Evidences that do not Support your Thoughts	Resultant Balanced, Realistic or Objective Thought	How do you feel now?

Thought Challenge

You can use this simple and effective approach to challenge your unhelpful thoughts. With this technique, you are able to view things from different perspectives using an evidence-based technique in the consideration of your various alternatives.

Rather than see this technique as just a form of positive affirmation, it is instead better considered as analyzing a thought objectively instead of accepting your thoughts to be pure facts or taking such facts to be true. Some of these thoughts tend to appear as facts which is why the act of challenging these thoughts is very important in trying to separate facts from friction.

Try and spend a lot of time on evidences that contradicts this kind of thoughts when using this worksheet.

What is the most intense and hot thought from the previous section you want to address?	
State the evidences you think supports this kind of thought?	

Do you have any evidence to contradict this thought?

How do you think you will feel, 6 months from now about this issue?

What alternative way of analyzing this situation can you think of?

What are the more objective, balanced and realistic way of viewing the situation?

Which of these do you consider more relevant?

How do you rate this new objective, balanced and realistic thought?

How does it make you now feel?

Is this an exercise you would want to try again? State your reason.

CBT General Worksheet

Describe the Situation	Note your Feelings and its Rating	Write your Automatic Negative Thoughts	Note Evidences Supporting your Thoughts	Evidences that do not Support your Thoughts	Resultant Balanced, Realistic or Objective Thought	How do you feel now?

Describe the Situation	Note your Feelings and its Rating	Write your Automatic Negative Thoughts	Note Evidences Supporting your Thoughts	Evidences that do not Support your Thoughts	Resultant Balanced, Realistic or Objective Thought	How do you feel now?

Describe the Situation	Note your Feelings and its Rating	Write your Automatic Negative Thoughts	Note Evidences Supporting your Thoughts	Evidences that do not Support your Thoughts	Resultant Balanced, Realistic or Objective Thought	How do you feel now?

Describe the Situation	Note your Feelings and its Rating	Write your Automatic Negative Thoughts	Note Evidences Supporting your Thoughts	Evidences that do not Support your Thoughts	Resultant Balanced, Realistic or Objective Thought	How do you feel now?

Describe the Situation	Note your Feelings and its Rating	Write your Automatic Negative Thoughts	Note Evidences Supporting your Thoughts	Evidences that do not Support your Thoughts	Resultant Balanced, Realistic or Objective Thought	How do you feel now?

Describe the Situation	Note your Feelings and its Rating	Write your Automatic Negative Thoughts	Note Evidences Supporting your Thoughts	Evidences that do not Support your Thoughts	Resultant Balanced, Realistic or Objective Thought	How do you feel now?

Describe the Situation	Note your Feelings and its Rating	Write your Automatic Negative Thoughts	Note Evidences Supporting your Thoughts	Evidences that do not Support your Thoughts	Resultant Balanced, Realistic or Objective Thought	How do you feel now?

Bridging Session Review

Dr's Name: _____   Date: _____

Session: _____   Date for Last Session: _____

What were the major points you gained from the last session?

What did you learn from it?

Was there anything between the last session and now that you'd like to talk about?

Is there any new development you would love to discuss?

Is there any aspect of the discussion you are not comfortable about?

Was there something you later regretted speaking about?

What is your mood right now compared to your last session? Do you consider it better or worse?

Great! So, what treatment goal would you want us to focus on today?

What emotion do you consider a top priority for now?

Did you attempt or do the exercises you were asked to do?

How did you find the exercises you had to do?

Would you say you benefited from it?

Status of Session

☐ End   ☐ Follow up

Remark

Thought Challenge

You can use this simple and effective approach to challenge your unhelpful thoughts. With this technique, you are able to view things from different perspectives using an evidence-based technique in the consideration of your various alternatives.

Rather than see this technique as just a form of positive affirmation, it is instead better considered as analyzing a thought objectively instead of accepting your thoughts to be pure facts or taking such facts to be true. Some of these thoughts tend to appear as facts which is why the act of challenging these thoughts is very important in trying to separate facts from friction.

Try and spend a lot of time on evidences that contradicts this kind of thoughts when using this worksheet.

What is the most intense and hot thought from the previous section you want to address?	
State the evidences you think supports this kind of thought?	

Do you have any evidence to contradict this thought?	

How do you think you will feel, 6 months from now about this issue?

What alternative way of analyzing this situation can you think of?

What are the more objective, balanced and realistic way of viewing the situation?

Which of these do you consider more relevant?

How do you rate this new objective, balanced and realistic thought?

How does it make you now feel?

Is this an exercise you would want to try again? State your reason.

CBT General Worksheet

Describe the Situation	Note your Feelings and its Rating	Write your Automatic Negative Thoughts	Note Evidences Supporting your Thoughts	Evidences that do not Support your Thoughts	Resultant Balanced, Realistic or Objective Thought	How do you feel now?

Describe the Situation	Note your Feelings and its Rating	Write your Automatic Negative Thoughts	Note Evidences Supporting your Thoughts	Evidences that do not Support your Thoughts	Resultant Balanced, Realistic or Objective Thought	How do you feel now?

Describe the Situation	Note your Feelings and its Rating	Write your Automatic Negative Thoughts	Note Evidences Supporting your Thoughts	Evidences that do not Support your Thoughts	Resultant Balanced, Realistic or Objective Thought	How do you feel now?

Describe the Situation	Note your Feelings and its Rating	Write your Automatic Negative Thoughts	Note Evidences Supporting your Thoughts	Evidences that do not Support your Thoughts	Resultant Balanced, Realistic or Objective Thought	How do you feel now?

Describe the Situation	Note your Feelings and its Rating	Write your Automatic Negative Thoughts	Note Evidences Supporting your Thoughts	Evidences that do not Support your Thoughts	Resultant Balanced, Realistic or Objective Thought	How do you feel now?

Describe the Situation	Note your Feelings and its Rating	Write your Automatic Negative Thoughts	Note Evidences Supporting your Thoughts	Evidences that do not Support your Thoughts	Resultant Balanced, Realistic or Objective Thought	How do you feel now?

Describe the Situation	Note your Feelings and its Rating	Write your Automatic Negative Thoughts	Note Evidences Supporting your Thoughts	Evidences that do not Support your Thoughts	Resultant Balanced, Realistic or Objective Thought	How do you feel now?

Thought Challenge

You can use this simple and effective approach to challenge your unhelpful thoughts. With this technique, you are able to view things from different perspectives using an evidence-based technique in the consideration of your various alternatives.

Rather than see this technique as just a form of positive affirmation, it is instead better considered as analyzing a thought objectively instead of accepting your thoughts to be pure facts or taking such facts to be true. Some of these thoughts tend to appear as facts which is why the act of challenging these thoughts is very important in trying to separate facts from friction.

Try and spend a lot of time on evidences that contradicts this kind of thoughts when using this worksheet.

What is the most intense and hot thought from the previous section you want to address?	
State the evidences you think supports this kind of thought?	

Do you have any evidence to contradict this thought?	

How do you think you will feel, 6 months from now about this issue?

What alternative way of analyzing this situation can you think of?

What are the more objective, balanced and realistic way of viewing the situation?

Which of these do you consider more relevant?

How do you rate this new objective, balanced and realistic thought?

How does it make you now feel?

Is this an exercise you would want to try again? State your reason.

CBT General Worksheet

Describe the Situation	Note your Feelings and its Rating	Write your Automatic Negative Thoughts	Note Evidences Supporting your Thoughts	Evidences that do not Support your Thoughts	Resultant Balanced, Realistic or Objective Thought	How do you feel now?

Describe the Situation	Note your Feelings and its Rating	Write your Automatic Negative Thoughts	Note Evidences Supporting your Thoughts	Evidences that do not Support your Thoughts	Resultant Balanced, Realistic or Objective Thought	How do you feel now?

Describe the Situation	Note your Feelings and its Rating	Write your Automatic Negative Thoughts	Note Evidences Supporting your Thoughts	Evidences that do not Support your Thoughts	Resultant Balanced, Realistic or Objective Thought	How do you feel now?

Describe the Situation	Note your Feelings and its Rating	Write your Automatic Negative Thoughts	Note Evidences Supporting your Thoughts	Evidences that do not Support your Thoughts	Resultant Balanced, Realistic or Objective Thought	How do you feel now?

Describe the Situation	Note your Feelings and its Rating	Write your Automatic Negative Thoughts	Note Evidences Supporting your Thoughts	Evidences that do not Support your Thoughts	Resultant Balanced, Realistic or Objective Thought	How do you feel now?

Describe the Situation	Note your Feelings and its Rating	Write your Automatic Negative Thoughts	Note Evidences Supporting your Thoughts	Evidences that do not Support your Thoughts	Resultant Balanced, Realistic or Objective Thought	How do you feel now?

Describe the Situation	Note your Feelings and its Rating	Write your Automatic Negative Thoughts	Note Evidences Supporting your Thoughts	Evidences that do not Support your Thoughts	Resultant Balanced, Realistic or Objective Thought	How do you feel now?

Bridging Session Review

Dr's Name: _____   Date: _____

Session: _____   Date for Last Session: _____

What were the major points you gained from the last session?

_____

What did you learn from it?

_____

Was there anything between the last session and now that you'd like to talk about?

_____

Is there any new development you would love to discuss?

_____

Is there any aspect of the discussion you are not comfortable about?

Was there something you later regretted speaking about?

What is your mood right now compared to your last session? Do you consider it better or worse?

Great! So, what treatment goal would you want us to focus on today?

What emotion do you consider a top priority for now?

Did you attempt or do the exercises you were asked to do?

How did you find the exercises you had to do?

Would you say you benefited from it?

Status of Session

[ ] End   [ ] Follow up

Remark

Thought Challenge

You can use this simple and effective approach to challenge your unhelpful thoughts. With this technique, you are able to view things from different perspectives using an evidence-based technique in the consideration of your various alternatives.

Rather than see this technique as just a form of positive affirmation, it is instead better considered as analyzing a thought objectively instead of accepting your thoughts to be pure facts or taking such facts to be true. Some of these thoughts tend to appear as facts which is why the act of challenging these thoughts is very important in trying to separate facts from friction.

Try and spend a lot of time on evidences that contradicts this kind of thoughts when using this worksheet.

What is the most intense and hot thought from the previous section you want to address?	
State the evidences you think supports this kind of thought?	

Do you have any evidence to contradict this thought?	

How do you think you will feel, 6 months from now about this issue?

What alternative way of analyzing this situation can you think of?

What are the more objective, balanced and realistic way of viewing the situation?

Which of these do you consider more relevant?

How do you rate this new objective, balanced and realistic thought?

How does it make you now feel?

Is this an exercise you would want to try again? State your reason.

CBT General Worksheet

Describe the Situation	Note your Feelings and its Rating	Write your Automatic Negative Thoughts	Note Evidences Supporting your Thoughts	Evidences that do not Support your Thoughts	Resultant Balanced, Realistic or Objective Thought	How do you feel now?

Describe the Situation	Note your Feelings and its Rating	Write your Automatic Negative Thoughts	Note Evidences Supporting your Thoughts	Evidences that do not Support your Thoughts	Resultant Balanced, Realistic or Objective Thought	How do you feel now?

Describe the Situation	Note your Feelings and its Rating	Write your Automatic Negative Thoughts	Note Evidences Supporting your Thoughts	Evidences that do not Support your Thoughts	Resultant Balanced, Realistic or Objective Thought	How do you feel now?

Describe the Situation	Note your Feelings and its Rating	Write your Automatic Negative Thoughts	Note Evidences Supporting your Thoughts	Evidences that do not Support your Thoughts	Resultant Balanced, Realistic or Objective Thought	How do you feel now?

Describe the Situation	Note your Feelings and its Rating	Write your Automatic Negative Thoughts	Note Evidences Supporting your Thoughts	Evidences that do not Support your Thoughts	Resultant Balanced, Realistic or Objective Thought	How do you feel now?

Describe the Situation	Note your Feelings and its Rating	Write your Automatic Negative Thoughts	Note Evidences Supporting your Thoughts	Evidences that do not Support your Thoughts	Resultant Balanced, Realistic or Objective Thought	How do you feel now?

Describe the Situation	Note your Feelings and its Rating	Write your Automatic Negative Thoughts	Note Evidences Supporting your Thoughts	Evidences that do not Support your Thoughts	Resultant Balanced, Realistic or Objective Thought	How do you feel now?

Thought Challenge

You can use this simple and effective approach to challenge your unhelpful thoughts. With this technique, you are able to view things from different perspectives using an evidence-based technique in the consideration of your various alternatives.

Rather than see this technique as just a form of positive affirmation, it is instead better considered as analyzing a thought objectively instead of accepting your thoughts to be pure facts or taking such facts to be true. Some of these thoughts tend to appear as facts which is why the act of challenging these thoughts is very important in trying to separate facts from friction.

Try and spend a lot of time on evidences that contradicts this kind of thoughts when using this worksheet.

What is the most intense and hot thought from the previous section you want to address?	
State the evidences you think supports this kind of thought?	

Do you have any evidence to contradict this thought?	

How do you think you will feel, 6 months from now about this issue?

What alternative way of analyzing this situation can you think of?

What are the more objective, balanced and realistic way of viewing the situation?

Which of these do you consider more relevant?

How do you rate this new objective, balanced and realistic thought?

How does it make you now feel?

Is this an exercise you would want to try again? State your reason.

CBT General Worksheet

Describe the Situation	Note your Feelings and its Rating	Write your Automatic Negative Thoughts	Note Evidences Supporting your Thoughts	Evidences that do not Support your Thoughts	Resultant Balanced, Realistic or Objective Thought	How do you feel now?

Describe the Situation	Note your Feelings and its Rating	Write your Automatic Negative Thoughts	Note Evidences Supporting your Thoughts	Evidences that do not Support your Thoughts	Resultant Balanced, Realistic or Objective Thought	How do you feel now?

Describe the Situation	Note your Feelings and its Rating	Write your Automatic Negative Thoughts	Note Evidences Supporting your Thoughts	Evidences that do not Support your Thoughts	Resultant Balanced, Realistic or Objective Thought	How do you feel now?

Describe the Situation	Note your Feelings and its Rating	Write your Automatic Negative Thoughts	Note Evidences Supporting your Thoughts	Evidences that do not Support your Thoughts	Resultant Balanced, Realistic or Objective Thought	How do you feel now?

Describe the Situation	Note your Feelings and its Rating	Write your Automatic Negative Thoughts	Note Evidences Supporting your Thoughts	Evidences that do not Support your Thoughts	Resultant Balanced, Realistic or Objective Thought	How do you feel now?

Describe the Situation	Note your Feelings and its Rating	Write your Automatic Negative Thoughts	Note Evidences Supporting your Thoughts	Evidences that do not Support your Thoughts	Resultant Balanced, Realistic or Objective Thought	How do you feel now?

Describe the Situation	Note your Feelings and its Rating	Write your Automatic Negative Thoughts	Note Evidences Supporting your Thoughts	Evidences that do not Support your Thoughts	Resultant Balanced, Realistic or Objective Thought	How do you feel now?

Bridging Session Review

Dr's Name: _____   Date: _____

Session: _____   Date for Last Session: _____

What were the major points you gained from the last session?

What did you learn from it?

Was there anything between the last session and now that you'd like to talk about?

Is there any new development you would love to discuss?

Is there any aspect of the discussion you are not comfortable about?

Was there something you later regretted speaking about?

What is your mood right now compared to your last session? Do you consider it better or worse?

Great! So, what treatment goal would you want us to focus on today?

What emotion do you consider a top priority for now?

Did you attempt or do the exercises you were asked to do?

How did you find the exercises you had to do?

Would you say you benefited from it?

Status of Session

☐ End   ☐ Follow up

Remark

Thought Challenge

You can use this simple and effective approach to challenge your unhelpful thoughts. With this technique, you are able to view things from different perspectives using an evidence-based technique in the consideration of your various alternatives.

Rather than see this technique as just a form of positive affirmation, it is instead better considered as analyzing a thought objectively instead of accepting your thoughts to be pure facts or taking such facts to be true. Some of these thoughts tend to appear as facts which is why the act of challenging these thoughts is very important in trying to separate facts from friction.

Try and spend a lot of time on evidences that contradicts this kind of thoughts when using this worksheet.

What is the most intense and hot thought from the previous section you want to address?	
State the evidences you think supports this kind of thought?	

Do you have any evidence to contradict this thought?	

How do you think you will feel, 6 months from now about this issue?

What alternative way of analyzing this situation can you think of?

What are the more objective, balanced and realistic way of viewing the situation?

Which of these do you consider more relevant?

How do you rate this new objective, balanced and realistic thought?

How does it make you now feel?

Is this an exercise you would want to try again? State your reason.

CBT General Worksheet

Describe the Situation	Note your Feelings and its Rating	Write your Automatic Negative Thoughts	Note Evidences Supporting your Thoughts	Evidences that do not Support your Thoughts	Resultant Balanced, Realistic or Objective Thought	How do you feel now?

Describe the Situation	Note your Feelings and its Rating	Write your Automatic Negative Thoughts	Note Evidences Supporting your Thoughts	Evidences that do not Support your Thoughts	Resultant Balanced, Realistic or Objective Thought	How do you feel now?

Describe the Situation	Note your Feelings and its Rating	Write your Automatic Negative Thoughts	Note Evidences Supporting your Thoughts	Evidences that do not Support your Thoughts	Resultant Balanced, Realistic or Objective Thought	How do you feel now?

Describe the Situation	Note your Feelings and its Rating	Write your Automatic Negative Thoughts	Note Evidences Supporting your Thoughts	Evidences that do not Support your Thoughts	Resultant Balanced, Realistic or Objective Thought	How do you feel now?

Describe the Situation	Note your Feelings and its Rating	Write your Automatic Negative Thoughts	Note Evidences Supporting your Thoughts	Evidences that do not Support your Thoughts	Resultant Balanced, Realistic or Objective Thought	How do you feel now?

Describe the Situation	Note your Feelings and its Rating	Write your Automatic Negative Thoughts	Note Evidences Supporting your Thoughts	Evidences that do not Support your Thoughts	Resultant Balanced, Realistic or Objective Thought	How do you feel now?

Describe the Situation	Note your Feelings and its Rating	Write your Automatic Negative Thoughts	Note Evidences Supporting your Thoughts	Evidences that do not Support your Thoughts	Resultant Balanced, Realistic or Objective Thought	How do you feel now?

Thought Challenge

You can use this simple and effective approach to challenge your unhelpful thoughts. With this technique, you are able to view things from different perspectives using an evidence-based technique in the consideration of your various alternatives.

Rather than see this technique as just a form of positive affirmation, it is instead better considered as analyzing a thought objectively instead of accepting your thoughts to be pure facts or taking such facts to be true. Some of these thoughts tend to appear as facts which is why the act of challenging these thoughts is very important in trying to separate facts from friction.

Try and spend a lot of time on evidences that contradicts this kind of thoughts when using this worksheet.

What is the most intense and hot thought from the previous section you want to address?	
State the evidences you think supports this kind of thought?	

Do you have any evidence to contradict this thought?

How do you think you will feel, 6 months from now about this issue?

What alternative way of analyzing this situation can you think of?

What are the more objective, balanced and realistic way of viewing the situation?

Which of these do you consider more relevant?

How do you rate this new objective, balanced and realistic thought?

How does it make you now feel?

Is this an exercise you would want to try again? State your reason.

CBT General Worksheet

Describe the Situation	Note your Feelings and its Rating	Write your Automatic Negative Thoughts	Note Evidences Supporting your Thoughts	Evidences that do not Support your Thoughts	Resultant Balanced, Realistic or Objective Thought	How do you feel now?

Describe the Situation	Note your Feelings and its Rating	Write your Automatic Negative Thoughts	Note Evidences Supporting your Thoughts	Evidences that do not Support your Thoughts	Resultant Balanced, Realistic or Objective Thought	How do you feel now?

Describe the Situation	Note your Feelings and its Rating	Write your Automatic Negative Thoughts	Note Evidences Supporting your Thoughts	Evidences that do not Support your Thoughts	Resultant Balanced, Realistic or Objective Thought	How do you feel now?

Describe the Situation	Note your Feelings and its Rating	Write your Automatic Negative Thoughts	Note Evidences Supporting your Thoughts	Evidences that do not Support your Thoughts	Resultant Balanced, Realistic or Objective Thought	How do you feel now?

Describe the Situation	Note your Feelings and its Rating	Write your Automatic Negative Thoughts	Note Evidences Supporting your Thoughts	Evidences that do not Support your Thoughts	Resultant Balanced, Realistic or Objective Thought	How do you feel now?

Describe the Situation	Note your Feelings and its Rating	Write your Automatic Negative Thoughts	Note Evidences Supporting your Thoughts	Evidences that do not Support your Thoughts	Resultant Balanced, Realistic or Objective Thought	How do you feel now?

Describe the Situation	Note your Feelings and its Rating	Write your Automatic Negative Thoughts	Note Evidences Supporting your Thoughts	Evidences that do not Support your Thoughts	Resultant Balanced, Realistic or Objective Thought	How do you feel now?

Bridging Session Review

Dr's Name: _____   Date: _____

Session: _____   Date for Last Session: _____

What were the major points you gained from the last session?

```
[                                                                    ]
[                                                                    ]
[                                                                    ]
[                                                                    ]
```

What did you learn from it?

```
[                                                                    ]
[                                                                    ]
[                                                                    ]
[                                                                    ]
```

Was there anything between the last session and now that you'd like to talk about?

```
[                                                                    ]
[                                                                    ]
[                                                                    ]
[                                                                    ]
[                                                                    ]
```

Is there any new development you would love to discuss?

```
[                                                                    ]
[                                                                    ]
[                                                                    ]
[                                                                    ]
[                                                                    ]
```

Is there any aspect of the discussion you are not comfortable about?

Was there something you later regretted speaking about?

What is your mood right now compared to your last session? Do you consider it better or worse?

Great! So, what treatment goal would you want us to focus on today?

What emotion do you consider a top priority for now?

Did you attempt or do the exercises you were asked to do?

How did you find the exercises you had to do?

Would you say you benefited from it?

Status of Session

☐ End   ☐ Follow up

Remark

Made in United States
Orlando, FL
01 December 2021

10937949R00065